Detective Dog™
and The Ghost

Detective Dog™
and The Ghost

Written by Leslie McGuire
Illustrated by Mitchell Rose

HOOKED ON
PHONICS™

Contents

Special Words

Special words help make this story fun.
Your child may need help reading them.

ghost

house

1 There Are No Ghosts

I am Detective Dog. I look for
lost pets. I get the pets back.

BAM! BAM! BAM!
I go to the door.
"Who is it?" I say.
It's Jack and Max.
Jack looks upset.
I say, "What's up, Jack?"

"My pet kitten is lost," says Jack.
"Can you get him back?"

"Yes, I can," I say. "Where did you last see him?"

"At the vet," says Jack, "but he is not there now."

"I think a ghost got him!"
says Max.

"There is a ghost in the house
on top of the hill," says Jack.
"I bet the ghost got my kitten."

"There are no ghosts," I say,
"but I will get the kitten back."

I set out for the house on the hill. I need to get Jack's kitten back and check out this ghost. Jack and Max do not know it, but there are NO ghosts!

I huff and puff up the hill. I do not see a ghost. But I do see a big house. It looks like a mess!

I go up to the house. Hmmm. There is no lock. I go into the house. That is when there is a C-R-A-C-K!

What is that?

I look here and there. Then I see an odd white thing by a box!

"Now what?" I think. "What can this white thing be?"

I go to check.
Then ZIP!
The white thing is GONE!

Did it go that way?
I look in back of
the box.
No white thing.
That's when...

WAP! ZAP! WAP!
I look! I see it! The white
thing skids by me and zips
into the kitchen!

I do not want to, but I go into the kitchen.

There are lots of cobwebs in there! Yuck! Cobwebs stick to me. I do not like this.

I see a jug with a big crack in it.
Then...

WAP! BAP! THUD!

The white thing zips by my leg!
I trip over the jug and slip. The
jug spills. Yuck!

I do not get it! I know there are
no ghosts.

"THERE ARE NO GHOSTS!" I say.
That's when I see the white thing
whiz by me! It goes up! WAY up!

3 It's a Ghost!

I need to sit down! I need to think. I get out my pad.

1. JACK'S KITTEN IS LOST.

2. THERE ARE NO GHOSTS!!!!!!

3. BUT THERE IS A WHITE THING.

4. IT ZIPS HERE AND THERE.

5. IT CAN GO UP.

"If the white thing can go up...,"
I say, "is it a ghost?"

A ghost?

I think I need to go up and see if it's a ghost or not.

"Here I come," I say.

I do NOT want to do this. But I am Detective Dog. I do what I say. I will get to the bottom of this.

That's when...

BONG! BONG! BONG!
Ack! I run. I run smack into a big clock! I look up. The ghost is on top of the clock!

I panic and drop my hat.
Then I run into the door.
That's when I see it!

"I bet there's a way to get rid
of ghosts," I say. "I will go back
to my house and look it up!"
That's when...

CLICK! CLICK! CLICK!
The clicks come from the stairs.
I look up. It's the ghost!
I bet it wants me to come up
the stairs!
What if it's a trap?

4ᴰ I Get It!

"You can run, and you can fly,"
I say to the ghost, "but you cannot
trap ME! I am Detective Dog!
I will NOT let a ghost trap me!
    "I will come up there NOW!"

Up I go....
I check the steps....

I make quick stops...

I look this way and that way....

At the top...I stop!
What will happen to me now?

But what is this thing? It's just a white blanket! What is in it?

That's when the kitten says,
Meow, MEOW! MEOW!

"I bet you are Jack's kitten,"
I say. "He will be glad to have you
back! Let's go!"

"Thanks, Detective Dog," says Jack. "You got my kitten back!"

"That's a good thing," says Max. "You are a good detective!"

"Yes," I say, "and...

THERE ARE NO GHOSTS!"